# How to Use the E

"Bee" a Good Listener!

Be as flexible and varied in the use of this book as you are in your teaching and your classroom. Adjust it to meet your needs.

A definite time may be scheduled for a class listening lesson. Or, perhaps it could be more effective to use these exercises with a smaller number of students as in a reading group.

As you read through the lessons, you may find some that will correlate directly with other areas you are studying in class. If so, use the listening lessons to introduce, supplement or even culminate the related unit.

These lessons can also be easily adapted for a listening center. Tape the lessons on a cassette. Place copies of the student pages, pencils and crayons in the center. (Provide a laminated answer key for the students to use to mark and/or correct their own papers.) And what an easy, no-more-work way to update a student who was absent on the day the lesson was assigned!

Younger students look up to, and are shy or hesitant to talk to, upper grade students. Use this as an opportunity to encourage rapport between the different grade levels by asking an upper grade student to read the lesson to your students.

Don't overlook a most valuable and eager resource - parent and/or grandparent volunteers. They may read the lesson to the students or prepare the tapes for your listening center. It will be a rewarding time for all!

The skill-based mini-activities that are on the bottom of some of the pages can

be easily used as supplemental activities for a related topic of study in other areas of the curriculum. These are also appropriate as seatwork assignments, brief "activities for the day," activities for those students who arrive at school early or must stay inside during recess or as a part of the learning center.

No matter how you choose to use these lessons, may you and your students find them beneficial, exciting and fun!

# The Hunt Is On!

Calie is a Calico cat with spots. She and her three friends are so bored! There is absolutely nothing to do! "Oh yes there is," says Calie's mother. "There will be two teams. Pick your partner." Then, she hands each team a list of eight items. They are going on a scavenger hunt!

1. Two rules are set for the hunt. The first is that they can only go to their friends' homes. The second is that there will be a time limit during which they can try to collect the items. Write **30 minutes** at the top of your paper.

2. Both teams read over their lists. The first item listed, a hairpin, has been in existence for 10,000 years. Originally, it was made from animal spines and thistle thorns. Bone, ivory, silver and even gold were used later. Some hairpins were plain and some were covered with jewels. Color the hairpin black. Write how many 0's there are in ten thousand under the hairpin.

3. Although bow ties became fashionable in the 1920's, men in Croatia, a republic in the northwest part of Yugoslavia, have been wearing them for hundreds of years. Color the bow tie a color that rhymes with fed.

4. How would you keep your coat buttoned if you had no buttons? Until about 3,000 years ago, people used straight pins to fasten their clothing. As fashions changed, more and more pins were needed. Draw a button around the safety pin.

5. Would you buy a drink of water from a vending machine even if it promised you a clean paper cup every time? In 1908, no one else would either! Why should people pay when they could get a free drink of water? Of course, everyone drank out of the same cup called a tin sipper. How unhealthy! A year later, the disposable paper cup business had become very successful. On the cup, write how many syllables there are in disposable.

6. When you scrub your hands, you are using a product that was first developed over 2,500 years ago. Soap today is very much like the original soap with only a few minor changes. Draw a bar of soap at the top left of the page.

7. Long ago, to keep hard candies fresh, people kept them in tin containers and later in tin foil. But in the late 1920's, aluminum was so inexpensive that it was used for wrapping hard candies. It was not until 1947, however, that aluminum foil was actually sold as it is today. On the piece of foil, write about how many years it took to sell aluminum foil from when it was first used to wrap candy.

8. Today, we wear these to protect our eyes and even to be fashionable. But the first dark glasses were worn by Chinese judges so that no one would be able to see their eye expressions during a trial. Color both the glasses and Calie black and yellow.

9. Although the very first of this item was provided by nature in the form of a clear pool of water, it became manmade using bronze metal. Write **It's me.** on the mirror. Color the tiger cat, Tyrone, orange.

10. Time's up! It's a tie! Each team found four of the items on the list. How many items did the cats find altogether? Write that number on the baseball hat. Now, everyone gets an ice cream cone. Draw a cone in each cat's hand.

    2     ©MCMXCIII Instructional Fair, Inc.

3

# What's That Sound?

After hearing so many of his friends talk about camping, a cat named Sidney is finally on his very first camping trip! The forest is so beautiful, peaceful and quiet . . . Wait a minute! What's that sound?

1. There is a scratching sound over there by the tree. Shhhhhh! That's the sound of the sharp claws of a skunk. Don't frighten a skunk. It can squirt a horrible-smelling fluid up to 12 feet away, and it rarely misses its target! Write **12 feet** on the skunk's tail.

2. Tap! Tap! Tap! A woodpecker is having its dinner. Its beak is drilling a hole so it can reach the insects that live in the tree bark. Draw a hole in the tree near the woodpecker's beak. Then, write an antonym for near on the tree. Color the woodpecker black and red.

3. Someone left the ice chest open and an opossum is looking for food. It doesn't seem worried that it has been noticed, otherwise it would go limp, shut its eyes, stick out its tongue and act like it is dead until it feels safe again. Write **playing opossum** on the ice chest. Color the opossum brown and its hat and the ice chest red.

4. Whoo-Whoo-Whoo-ah! That was a barred owl. Its nickname is hoot owl because of the sound it makes. Write the name of your favorite bird over the owl. Color it grey.

5. There's something on the tent! Boy, is it noisy and active! It's a red squirrel. It only weighs about half of a pound. On the side of the tent, write how many ounces are in a pound. Color the squirrel red and the tent green.

6. What's that croaking sound? It's a tailless frog with bulging eyes. Color it green. Then, on the back of your paper, write three words that rhyme with frog.

7. Sidney looks up and sees a full moon. He wonders why, on some nights, it's a thin slice of light. But the moon doesn't change its size or shape. It only appears to. The sun lights the moon in different parts depending on the time of the month. Color the moon yellow.

8. Sidney looks out his tent and sees what looks like a masked bandit. Now he is really scared! In the moon's bright light, he sees that it is only a raccoon. On the back of your paper, write an adjective that describes a raccoon.

9. A raccoon can have seven rings on its tail. Count how many rings the raccoon has in the picture. On the flag, write how many more it needs to make seven. Color the lake blue.

10. Now that Sidney knows what is making all the noise, he can go to sleep. Color Sidney orange and the trees green.

## Follow-Up Fun

Write the following phrases on a chalkboard with these directions:
Read each phrase. Write a word or words that describe the sound the objects in the phrases would make. These can be real words or words created by you.

1. a book falling off a shelf
2. someone running their fingernails across the chalkboard
3. a can of soda pop being poured into a glass
4. an ice cube being dropped into a glass
5. a mosquito flying near your ear
6. someone trying to get ketchup out of a bottle

4

# Now, That's a Cake!

The class is having a bake sale to earn money for a special field trip. All of the students decide to bake the cakes, cookies and brownies themselves. That afternoon, Calie and some of her friends meet at Sidney's house. They decide to make one special cake together.

1. Calie begins by opening the box of the cake mix. Write your favorite kind of cake on the cake box label. Color Calie's outfit green.

2. Sidney gets three eggs from the refrigerator. Draw three eggs on the counter. Oooops! One of the eggs is cracked. Write the number word of how many eggs Sidney has left on the refrigerator.

3. They will need a measuring cup to measure the vegetable oil. Draw a measuring cup half full of vegetable oil on the counter.

4. It's going to be a two-layer cake. Write three words that rhyme with cake on the back of the page.

5. The recipe also calls for a half cup of water. Draw water coming out of the faucet. Color it blue. $H_2O$ is the chemical equation for water. Write $H_2O$ in the sink.

6. The oven must be preheated. Patrick is setting the oven to 350°. Draw a line from the center of the temperature dial to 350°.

7. Patrick is bored. Calie lets him count out the marshmallows. Draw eight marshmallows on the counter next to Patrick. Color three yellow, three blue and two red.

8. Heidi really likes jellybeans. She wants jellybeans in the cake too. Draw a candy jar with six jellybeans in Heidi's right hand. Subtract the number of jellybeans from the number of marshmallows. Write that number above Heidi's head.

9. Oh my! Everyone likes chocolate chips. There must be chocolate chips in the cake! Draw five chocolate chips in the mixing bowl. Add the number of chocolate chips, jellybeans and marshmallows together and write that number on the mixer.

10. On the back of the paper, draw and color what a slice of this cake will look like.

**Follow-Up Fun**

Write the following directions on your chalkboard as an Activity of the Day.

Pretend that your class is making a special cake for a bake sale. The cake will be cut into twelve slices and sold by the slice. Answer the following questions:

•What special ingredients would you want to add to the cake?

•How many of each ingredient would you want in each slice?

•How many of each ingredient would you need to put in for the whole cake?

•How much would you sell a slice of cake for?

•If you sold all twelve slices at the price you wanted to, how much would you make?

•Draw a picture of a slice of this special cake.

7

# Ought To Be an Otter

While visiting the California coastal area, Tyrone, the tiger cat, and Sidney see nature's very own aquarium. What a view they have!

1. Tyrone wants a close-up view of the different animals. Draw a pair of binoculars in one of Tyrone's hands. Color Tyrone's clothes orange. He has the number one on his shirt.

2. By the rocky shoreline is a kelp bed. This brownish seaweed is attached to the rocks by a threadlike stem called a holdfast. The plant grows from the holdfast and forms leaves which float on the surface of the ocean. Holdfast is a compound word. On the back of your paper, write three compound words.

3. Floating in the kelp bed is a furry sea otter. Its large, thick fur coat keeps it warm because it doesn't have a layer of fat or blubber like other animals. It must clean and groom its fur many times during the day in order to keep air trapped in it. Find the sea otter floating on its back. Color its head, throat and neck white. Color the rest of its body brown.

4. Sea otters weigh up to 80 pounds. They need to eat a lot of food - about 20 pounds a day! This gives them the energy they need to keep their bodies warm. They often dive to the bottom of the ocean in search of food and pick up a rock which they use as a tool. Draw a rock in the diving otter's paw. How many pounds of food will an otter eat in a week? Write the answer under the otter.

5. One way the otter uses the rock is to loosen an abalone's hold on a large rock. The holes in the top of an abalone's shell release the water that was taken in under the shell to provide it with oxygen. Its shell is camouflaged for protection. On the back of your paper, write six new words using the letters in the word camouflaged.

6. Sea cucumbers are another favorite food of the sea otter. Even though they look like the vegetable called cucumber, they are animals. Write your favorite vegetable over the sea otter.

7. The sea otter eats ten different types of clams. The clam's body is protected by two shells which open and close when a muscle between its shells relaxes or tightens. Write the number **10** backwards under the clam.

8. The large rocks along the coastline make perfect homes for barnacles and the perfect supermarket for otters. Thousands of barnacles firmly attach themselves to the rocks by the head part of their bodies. Find the rocks covered by barnacles. Write **supermarket** on them.

9. Squids are a special treat for the sea otter. However, their body shape, eight arms and two tentacles, make them fast swimmers. When in danger, they can change color and squirt a cloud of dark ink into the water. Ooops! Too many otters here! Color the squid blue and Sidney yellow.

10. Once the sea otter has collected its food, it returns to the surface, rolls on its back, places its meal on its chest and enjoys eating its catch. Today's snack - a sea urchin. This animal's colorful, rounded or heart-shaped shell is covered with spines. Ouch! Be careful! Color the sea urchin orange. On the back of your paper, write an antonym for colorful.

9

# Worth Its Weight in Gold!

While vacationing in Nevada, Calie and Sidney visited the old mining town of Virginia City. It was as if they had taken a walk back in time. They listened carefully as an old miner showed and explained to them how his great-great grandfather panned for gold back in 1850.

1.  Every miner needed a good pair of sturdy boots for walking over the hard, rocky ground and wading in the cold river water. Draw a pair of boots on the miner. Write a synonym for sturdy under the miner.

2.  A mule was of utmost importance. Not only could the miner ride it, but he/she could also use it to carry or pack all of the needed tools and supplies on it. Draw a mule in the lower right corner of the picture. Color it brown.

3.  To separate more of the dirt and clay from the gold at a faster rate, many miners used a sluice box. This is a three-sided trough from which water constantly flows. The original sluice boxes were made of wood. Color the outside of the sluice box brown. Draw a three-sided shape under the sluice box.

4.  A shovel was used to put dirt, clay and rock into the top, or head, of the sluice box. Draw a shovel in front of the sluice box. Next to the shovel, write the name of another tool one might have used to pan for gold.

5.  Draw small rocks, clay and dirt at the top of the sluice box. Color them brown and grey. Think of a word opposite of small. Draw a rock that size at the bottom of the sluice box.

6.  There are small dams called riffles spaced every few inches apart along the bottom of the sluice box. These trap gold and heavier rocks. Draw six rocks in one of the riffles. Color them grey.

7.  When it's time to clean up, the riffles are lifted out. Draw a riffle next to Sidney. Color Sidney's clothes yellow.

8.  A bucket of water is used to wash the gold and other rocks out of the riffle and into a gold pan. Draw a bucket of water in Calie's hand. Color Calie's clothes blue.

9.  The riffle is held over a gold pan. The gold pan is 8-24 inches in diameter and 2-3 inches deep. The sides of the pan slope from the rim to the bottom of the pan. Draw a gold pan between Calie and Sidney. Under that pan, write how many inches are in a foot.

10. The gold pan is then slightly tipped and gently moved back and forth as the water is poured out. Because gold is heavy, it settles in the bottom of the gold pan. Draw seven gold nuggets in the gold pan. Color them bright yellow. Write **seven** above the gold pan.

## Follow-Up Fun

Write the following directions on the chalkboard or on a sheet of paper for homework or extra credit.

**Graph the Gold!** Many of the cats were panning for gold. After cleaning up, the miner weighed their nuggets. The cats had panned the following in ounces: Calie - 4, Sidney - 9, Tyrone - 6, Max - 5, Bernice - 7 and Alison - 2. Use these amounts to make a bar graph of what the miner recorded.

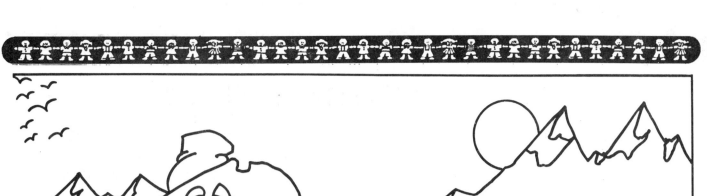

11

# Sail Away

Today, cars, buses, planes and even spacecraft take us anywhere in a relatively short amount of time. But how did people travel long ago? Pretend that you are visiting a museum that has life-size models of transportation used throughout history. The first huge room is filled with historic boats and ships that were once used to travel along rivers and across seas.

1. Not only did the prehistoric people use animal skins for their clothing, but they also used them to make small round-shaped boats called coracles. These boats were waterproofed by a coating of tar. Waterproofed is a compound word. Write three compound words on the back of your paper.

2. Egyptians used large boats to transport goods up and down the Nile River. These heavy crafts were driven only by a sail. Write **windy** on the sail of the Egyptian trading boat. Write north, south, east and west in the correct locations on the page.

3. The Egyptians used a rectangular sail called a square sail. On the sail of the Egyptian trading boat, draw two more shapes. Color the boat brown.

4. Bundles of reed were tied together by the Egyptians to make the small boats that were used for daily fishing. Write three words above the small boat that rhyme with reed. Color the small Egyptian fishing boat brown.

5. The Vikings used one type of boat for trading and another for attacking and robbing. The boats used for attacking had a dragon's head carved on one or both of its ends. Draw a circle around the dragon's head. Color the boat black.

6. Because they traveled great distances from their homes in Norway, Sweden and Denmark, the Vikings relied on the wind to push their brightly-colored sails. Color the Viking ship's sail red and blue. Write the name of a body of water in the area above the Viking war ship.

7. When the wind was calm or the Vikings were nearing land for an attack, the ship had to be rowed. Thirty-two men were needed, sixteen on each side, to row. The oars were extended through holes on the sides of the ship. If there were sixteen men and eight oars on each side of the ship, how many men were there to each oar? Write that number under the Viking war ship.

8. Shields mounted to the sides of the ship provided the only protection for the Viking rowers. Color three shields your favorite colors. On the back of your paper, write **favorite**. Then, write three new words using the letters in that word.

9. The early explorers also needed ships that could carry supplies needed for a long period of time because they weren't exactly sure where they were going or how long it would take them to get there. Draw a barrel on the explorers' ship. Color it black and the ship brown.

10. Sailors were always on duty watching for land. They climbed ropes to reach the enclosed platform high on the ship's mast called the crow's-nest. Write **Land ahead!** between the two masts, or tall poles, of the explorers' ship.

## Follow-Up Fun

Have the students select one of the types of boats of long ago and construct it using any materials they prefer.

12

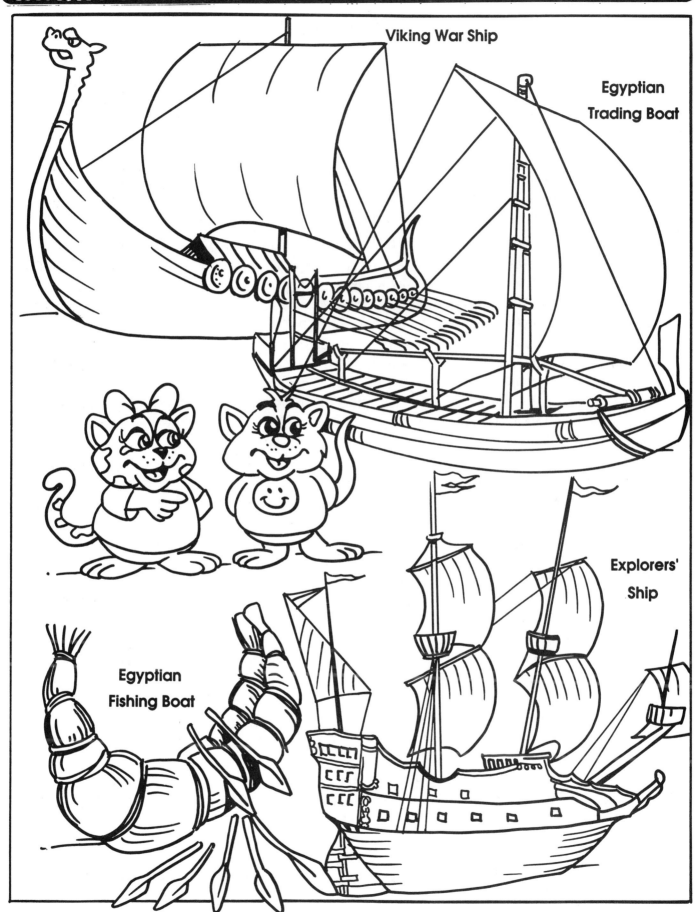

Viking War Ship

Egyptian
Trading Boat

Explorers'
Ship

Egyptian
Fishing Boat

13

# Cryptic Codes

Someone had dropped a torn piece of paper on the floor. Calie shook her head and picked it up. As she walked toward the trash can, she looked at the paper. Every letter was written very carefully, but the letters didn't spell any recognizable words - Hmmmmm. Oh! Of course! It was a coded message. Being very curious, Calie decided to go to the library to find out more about cryptography, or secret writing.

1. Calie decided to start by looking in the encyclopedia. Cryptography begins with the letter c. Write the missing letters of the alphabet on the books on the middle shelf. On the top of the bookshelf, write how many syllables there are in the word cryptography.

2. When Calie found the word cryptography, the book said to look under codes and ciphers. Write **codes** in the speech bubble. Color Calie orange.

3. Long ago, the Spartans used a stick and a belt to write messages. The belt was wound around a stick and the message was written along one side. Then, the belt was removed. Unless a person had exactly the same size stick, the message could not be decoded. Draw a stick on the table. Write the two words that make up the word message above the stick.

4. A grille, which was a card with holes in it, was used in the 1500's and 1600's. The person writing the message placed the grille on top of a blank sheet of paper, wrote the secret message in the cut-out spaces, lifted off the grille and then filled the page with words so that it would appear as a normal letter. Only the person with an identical grille could read the secret message. Draw three boxes on the standing book next to Calie's left hand. Color one red, one yellow and one blue.

5. If a message is written in code, each word is changed to another word. A code book is needed to decode, or translate, the message. Write **code book** on the bottom, closed book.

6. Ciphers are written by changing each of the letters in the word. Sometimes the letters are written as numbers. The letter A would be the number 1, B - 2, C - 3 and so on through the alphabet. Number the letters on the set of encyclopedias from 1 to 26. Write each number in the space above the letter.

7. Another substitution cipher is to number the letters of the alphabet backwards. The letter Z would be numbered 1, Y - 2, X - 3 through the alphabet ending with the letter A being 26. In the spaces below the letters on the encyclopedias, number the letters from 1 to 26 beginning with the letter Z.

8. Sometimes each letter is substituted by a different letter. These cryptograms are hard to decipher unless you know which letters represent the ones in the message. In the upper right corner of the shelf, write a question mark and in the bottom right corner, write an exclamation point.

9. One of the simplest ways to make a cipher is to substitute the real letter for the one that comes after it in the alphabet. Cat would be "dbu." Decode the message on the paper using this method.

10. Draw a big star on the top of the paper with the secret message.

**Follow-Up Fun**
Let students develop their own secret codes and messages using them. Put copies of the coded messages in a center for students to "break."

15

# Whale Watching

Sidney's Uncle Chester has invited Sidney and his friends to go whale watching on his boat. After sailing offshore, Uncle Chester stops the boat.

1. To keep the boat from drifting, Uncle Chester drops the anchor over the side. Draw a chain from the boat to the water with an anchor on the end. Color the boat brown.

2. The right whale is a baleen whale because it has no teeth. Instead, it has hundreds of thin plates in its mouth called baleen. Baleen is made of the same material that your fingernails are made of. Color the right whale black. On the back of your paper, write five parts of your body.

3. Narwhals are the only whales with horns or tusks. They have a tooth that grows through their upper lip. Color the narwhal gray with black spots on its back and the tusk yellow. On the bottom of the page, write the name of another animal that has a tusk.

4. Blue whales are considered the largest animals. They can grow to a length of 100 feet and weigh up to 220 short tons. Sometimes they are called sulfur-bottom whales because distoms, tiny plants, often grow on their stomachs forming a yellow film. Color the blue whale blue with a yellow stomach.

5. A short ton equals 2,000 pounds. If the blue whale weighs 220 short tons, how much does the blue whale weigh in pounds? Write the answer above the blue whale.

6. At one time, the beluga whale was called a "sea canary" because it makes a birdlike sound which can be heard above the water. It makes growling and roaring sounds too. Color the beluga whale white. It is chasing the squid which it loves to eat.

7. Instead of having a dorsal fin on its back, the gray whale has a row of small humps. Their gray or black bodies have crescent-shaped marks on them. The gray whale is the whale above the squid. Draw a crescent, or moon shape, on the whale and color it gray.

8. Perhaps the humpback whale was named for the way it humps its back as it dives in the ocean. These playful whales roll over, leap, even slap each other and make so much noise that they can be heard several miles away. One humpback whale swam through the San Francisco Bay and into the fresh water of the Sacramento River. Concerned people worked to direct him back to the bay and out to sea to join the other migrating whales. They called him Humphrey. Write a capital H on the humpback whale's back.

9. The killer whale, really a large dolphin, is definitely appropriately named. It is an avid hunter, eating seals, penguins, dolphins, squid, fish and even other killer whales if they are injured. However, there has never been a recorded incident of a killer whale attacking a human. Write **hunter** above the killer whale. The killer whale is black with white spots on it. Color it.

10. The bottle-nosed dolphins are members of the whale family. They are frequently seen performing at many marine parks. Since researchers found that bottle-nosed dolphins make different sounds to communicate with each other, they have been trying to find ways that humans can communicate with them. Draw a big star on the bottle-nosed dolphin. It's the one jumping out of the ocean.

16

bottle-nosed dolphin

narwhal

humpback whale

porpoise

blue whale

gray whale

right whale

killer whale

beluga
whale

# Nutty Nibblers

Tyrone has invited his friends to watch a new movie video, *The Mystery of Inspector Frederick Feline*. But, what can they munch on while watching the movie? Popcorn? No, he wants something different! Calie has a special munchies recipe and is willing to help Tyrone prepare it.

1. First, they melt one cube of margarine in the large pan. Draw a cube of margarine in the pan. Color it yellow.

2. Next, they add 1/4 teaspoon of the first seasoning people are known to have used - salt. It was once so valuable that Roman soldiers were given special rations of salt called salarium, meaning salt money. This is where we got our word for salary. Draw a dollar sign on the salt container. On the top of that container, write how many pennies are in a dollar.

3. Now it is time to add fruit kernels, or seeds, which of course are nuts. Calie and Tyrone add one cup of sweet almonds. The other kind of almonds are bitter and are only used for flavoring. Write **sweet** on the package of almonds. Then, write an antonym for sweet at the top left of the page.

4. Next, one cup of cashews is added. Thank goodness these are roasted! Cashews have an oil between their outer and inner shells which is poisonous and can irritate a person's skin. Roasting removes the oil. Did you know that the cashew is related to poison ivy? Write **roasted** on the package of cashews. Color the box red.

5. Another cup of nuts is added. This time, it's walnuts. Black walnuts have such a hard shell that they are already shelled and packaged before people buy them. Color the walnut package black.

6. Calie and Tyrone add a cup of peanuts next which really are not nuts at all! They are called groundnuts because they grow under the ground and not on a tree. On the back of your paper, write five words using the letters in peanut.

7. Now for literally an award-winning ingredient - 2 cups of pretzels. Long ago, when the Turkish armies were attacking Vienna in the 1500's, they couldn't get over the wall that surrounded the town. So, they decided to dig under it. The Viennese bakers, wanting fresh pretzels for the next day, were busy baking all night. When they heard digging sounds, they reported them, and the town's army stopped the Turkish army from invading. A medal or coat of arms with a pretzel emblem on it was awarded to the bakers. Draw a prize medal on the box of pretzels.

8. Two cups of a crunchy cereal need to be added now. It's hard to imagine that cold cereal wasn't a favorite family breakfast food until the 1890's. On top of the TV, write how many ounces are in a cup.

9. Add one teaspoon of a sauce that was brought over from India in the 1800's. Color the bottle of worcestershire sauce brown. Below the bottle, write how many syllables are in worcestershire.

10. Only a few drops of the spicy ingredient, Tabasco sauce, are needed. When Edmund McIhenny returned to his in-laws' plantation after the Civil War, the only thing not destroyed was a crop of capsicum peppers. He used the peppers to create a new sauce. He named it after the Tabasco River in Mexico. Color the Tabasco bottle red because it's hot and spicy.

# Come in Costume

Usually when invited to a costume party, you think about dressing as a clown, monster or even an alien. Samantha's party is just a little bit different. Everyone is to wear a costume based on history.

1. Reginald likes to go barefoot, so he chose the clothing worn by prehistoric people, who probably lived 2 million years ago. Mammoths, bison, bear and deer skins were used for clothing back then. Color the caveman's clothes brown. On his bone, write how many zero's are in one million.

2. Prehistoric people also wore jewelry. Like the clothing, jewelry was made from animals. Tusks, bones and teeth from animals were strung to make necklaces. Color the teeth necklace yellow. Count how many teeth are on the necklace. Write that number above the caveman's head.

3. Samantha, fascinated by the mystery of the Egyptian pyramids, wore the cool, white, straight linen dress of the Egyptians. Both men and women wore wigs made from human hair or wool at this time. Color Samantha orange and her dress white. Don't color her collar.

4. Make-up, such as lipstick, rouge and eye shadow, was worn by both Egyptian men and women back then. Beaded collars were also a common form of jewelry. Color Samantha's collar alternating blue and purple.

5. The Romans! Their culture and influence spread far around the world. Sidney chose clothing that could have been worn by a member of the senate in Rome. He wore a tunic draped over a toga. His tunic and toga are trimmed in a purple band. Purple could only be worn by wealthy people because purple dye was very expensive. Color the toga and the trim around the neck and edge of the tunic purple.

6. The tunics that the Romans wore were different lengths. The Roman soldiers always wore the tunic short. Write the name of one of our armed services at the bottom of the page.

7. Patrick liked the horned helmets of the Vikings. The helmet was made of metal pieces that allowed a person to see, yet it also protected the face. Color Patrick orange and his helmet grey.

8. After the Viking men sheared the sheep, the women spent time cleaning, spinning and weaving the wool into materials to be used for dresses, tunics and pants. Color Patrick's tunic shirt red and his pants brown.

9. The fashions of the French court in the 1700's were very elegant. Calie liked the dresses that stuck out far (with the use of a frame called a panier). Women who wore these had to turn sideways to get through a doorway! Sideways and doorway are compound words. Write three compound words on Calie's dress. Then, color the dress blue.

10. The most extraordinary part of Calie's costume was her wig. Elaborate wigs worn at that time had feathers, flowers or almost anything imaginable worked into the wig. The person's real hair was combined with false hair and combed over a wire frame to create a very tall and impressive hairstyle. Hairpins and grease held the style in place for weeks. There was only one problem. Lice and fleas often settled in these artistic creations. Write **It itches!** on Calie's wig.

21

# Powerful and Swift

It's a beautiful day to visit a wildlife park. Samantha and some of her friends arrived just in time to watch the presentation about birds of prey.

1. Mr. Orin, the ranger, explains that the birds he will be showing and talking about are hunters among bird species. That is why they are called birds of prey. These types of birds are also known as carnivores, or meat eaters. Write **meat eaters** between the bald eagle's wings.

2. Long ago, falcons and hawks were trained to help men hunt food. Today, laws have been passed which protect these birds. Special permission is required before a person may own one of these birds. Write two words that have the prefix **pro** as in protect on the back of your paper.

3. A peregrine falcon is one of the fastest flying birds. It dives at speeds of up to 180 miles per hour. On the falcon on the ranger's arm, write how fast this bird can go in one minute.

4. A peregrine falcon's sharp, strong claws, or talons, grip Mr. Orin's gloved hand. Color the thick, padded glove brown. Then, color the falcon tan and brown.

5. Red-tail hawks have beautiful reddish tail feathers. They also have sharp eyesight - about eight times as sharp as humans! Color the ranger's outfit green.

6. Every fall, red-tail hawks migrate south in large groups called kettles. Another meaning of kettle is a tea kettle or a teapot. Write another homonym like kettle on the back of your paper.

7. That beautiful bird landing behind Mr. Orin is a bald eagle. Long ago, in England, the word bald was spelled with a "t" at the end and meant white-headed. Color the bald eagle's head white and its feathers brown.

8. Most birds of prey eat rodents, birds and small animals. Bald eagles prefer fish. Draw a fish to the right of the bald eagle.

9. The bald eagle became the national symbol for the United States in 1782. Write how many years ago that was to the left of the bald eagle.

10. A picture of the bald eagle can be found on U.S. coins, paper money and, of course, government seals. Above the eagle's tail, write who is on the front of a penny.

## Follow-Up Fun
Write the directions below on the chalkboard as an extra credit activity or homework for your class.

## Eyesight Excellence
All birds of prey have excellent eyesight. Make a wordsearch that includes all of the words in the list to the right. Exchange puzzles with a friend. Then, use your excellent eyesight to "hunt" for and circle the words in the puzzle. •Hide the name of a secret bird in your puzzle and see if your friend can find it without telling him/her the name of the bird.

### Word Bank

| | |
|---|---|
| birds | hunters |
| carnivore | kettles |
| eagle | rodents |
| falcon | speed |
| fish | talon |
| hawk | wildlife |

23

# Create a Castle

For a few hours every Wednesday afternoon, Calie baby-sits Arnie Abyssinian while his mother does volunteer work at the hospital. Calie and Arnie always have a lot of fun together. Today is no exception. Arnie and Calie are putting together a miniature castle set that his grandmother sent him.

1.  Castles are actually forts that were built to protect the land owned by very wealthy men called lords. Many were built on top of steep hills. Others were built on smaller hills surrounded by outer walls made of stone. For additional protection, a deep ditch was dug around the castle itself. The ditch, or moat, was filled with water. Color the water blue.

2.  A drawbridge, a bridge that could be raised or lowered, allowed residents and welcomed guests to enter and leave the castle. Write **Welcome** on the road leading to the drawbridge.

3.  If, by chance, an enemy was able to sneak across the drawbridge, a gate made of iron bars called a portcullis could be lowered to block the entrance to the castle. On the back of your paper, write **portcullis**. Then, write four new words using the letters in that word.

4.  Because each of the landlords was always trying to take possession of everyone else's property, a large percentage of the castle's residents were soldiers. Write **Now Hiring** on the castle walls.

5.  The soldiers patrolled the walls and towers day and night. Alternating open spaces and solid walls lined the castle's walls. Soldiers shot arrows through the open spaces and hid behind the solid walls called merlons for protection from arrows. If the soldiers patrolled the wall day and night, how many hours in a day did they patrol? Write the answer on the tower to the right of the drawbridge.

6.  Many people were needed to take care of the castle and provide food for the soldiers, the landlord and his family. Gardeners planted, cared for and harvested vegetables and herbs. Draw six peas in the garden plot. Color them green.

7.  With the aid of trained dogs and hawks, the huntsmen were able to provide fresh meat for the castle residents. Draw a dog in the space between the outer wall and a bird flying in the sky.

8.  Color Calie's clothes a color that rhymes with Fred and color Arnie's clothes a color that rhymes with fellow.

9.  Donkeys were also used to help provide necessities. They walked inside a large wheel that raised a bucket to bring up water from a well. Draw a well in the middle of the castle courtyard. Color the castle grey and the grass green.

10. Of course, craftsmen were needed to make and repair the armor, shields and swords used by the soldiers and knights. Draw a shield on the small building that is inside the castle courtyard. Color the shield yellow and the building blue.

**Follow-Up Fun**
Have students design a special castle that they would liked to have lived in a long time ago. Display them with the title: **Castles of Dreams**

CASTLE SET

TIGER

# Captivating Caverns

When Sidney told Calie he was a spelunker, she thought he meant he was an alien from outer space. Sidney explained that a spelunker is a person who explores caves. Then, he invited her to go spelunking, or cave exploring, with him. What they saw in the cave was fascinating!

1. Sidney explained that the cave began forming when water seeped through cracks in the limestone rock. Slowly, over thousands of years, the rock was dissolved by the acid that was formed when the carbon dioxide in the air and ground mixed with the water. Draw a drop of water dripping from the ceiling of the cave. Color it blue.

2. Caves are very dark and damp inside. Plants cannot grow inside a cave, but some ferns and moss plants may grow directly outside of the cave entrance where there is sunlight. Color the fern and the moss plants green.

3. As Calie enters the cave, she looks at the wall and the floor. It is covered with flowstone which is the name for layers of minerals that are left on the wall and floor when water flows over them. Flowstone is a compound word. Write the two words that make up flowstone on top of the page.

4. When the minerals in the water crystallize, they form different shapes called speleothems. The pointed speleothems hanging from the ceiling that look like icicles are called stalactites. Color five stalactites blue.

5. The pointed pillars developing from the floor and raising upward are called stalagmites. Color four stalagmites blue.

6. Sidney calls Calie over to see a column which is formed when a stalactite and stalagmite join together. Subtract the number of stalagmites you colored from the number of stalactites you colored. Write that number to the left of the mushroom.

7. The layers of rock that are hanging from the ceiling look like drapes which is why they are called drapery. Color the drapery brown.

8. Being well-equipped for cave exploration is a must. Calie and Sidney wore heavy clothes to keep them warm and hard hats to protect their heads from jagged rocks. They also brought lights so that they are able to see inside the dark cave. Draw a headlight on Calie's hard hat and a flashlight in Sidney's hand. Color the lights yellow.

9. As they go farther and farther into the deep part of the cave, Calie and Sidney find some troglobites. Troglobites are spiders, salamanders, beetles and other animals that live in caves. Their thin skin lacks any color, and they have excellent senses of smell and touch. However, most of them are blind. Color the troglobites grey.

10. What was that? Time to go! Another cave-dwelling animal, a bat, has just flown over their heads. Draw a bat flying over Calie's and Sidney's heads. Color it black. On the back of your paper, write four words that rhyme with bat.

**Follow-Up Fun**
Have students draw a cave scene with stalactites and stalagmites. They should write facts about caves on the stalactites and opinions about caves on the stalagmites.

27

# Admirable Ancients

All the students have completed their research about ancient civilizations. Now it's time to present their oral reports. Each student has made a large mural to use as a visual aid to help others understand.

1. Patrick learned about the Maya Indian Empire which was located in Mexico and in northern parts of Central America. Write north, south, east and west in their correct places on the map. Use the first initial.

2. The Mayan pyramids had roof-comb which were like flat steeples. These were very decorative, and made the pyramid appear extremely tall. The pyramid at Tikal measured 212 feet high. Write the number 212 above the pyramid. Also, write the abbreviation for feet behind the number.

3. Symbols which represented events, names and dates were developed as a form of writing. Count the number of steps on the pyramid. Write that number on the third step of the pyramid. Color the pyramid yellow.

4. The Aztecs, who built their empire in Mexico during the 1400's and 1500's, intrigued Sidney. Tenochtitlan, the capital city, was built on an island in Lake Texcoco. It was the major market place where trading was the daily activity. People either carried their goods to market or transported them in a dugout canoe along one of the many canals. Color the canoe brown.

5. Obsidian, volcanic glass, was one of the major items traded. It was used for making knives. Draw two knives to the left of the Aztecian in the canoe.

6. One of the Aztecs' basic foods was one you enjoy today. It was a very thin pancake made from corn called a tlaxcalli. Perhaps you know it better by the Spanish word - tortilla. They filled the tlaxcallis with meat and vegetables and made tacos. Color the corn yellow, the Aztecian brown and the water blue.

7. Trading was very popular among the Aztecs. One item was usually traded for another item, or sometimes services were traded. Money, such as coins and bills, did not exist. Instead, cacao beans, used for making chocolate drinks, were used as a form of money. Color the cacao beans brown. Count the cacao beans in the picture. If one cacao bean equals 25 cents, write how much money there is to the right of the Aztecian.

8. The western coast of South America was the home of the Inca Empire. Calie was amazed by the suspension bridges and roads that were built to connect the different parts of the Incan Empire. People walked and carried whatever they had to sell, or they loaded their goods on llamas. Color the llama brown and white.

9. Public buildings and homes of the Incas were made of stone or adobe blocks. These were cut so perfectly that they fit together without the use of cement or any other materials. Color the stones of the house yellow and the thatched roof brown.

10. Incans did not have a written language. Colored strings with various knots were attached to a cord to provide a system for keeping records of food, supplies, births, deaths, goods and weapons. The cords of knotted strings were called quipus. No one today has been able to understand how to interpret the quipus. On the back of your paper, write the day, month and year you were born.

**Mayans**

North America

South America

**Aztecs**

North America

South America

**Incas**

South America

# Practicing Puppeteers

Tomorrow morning, Samantha and her friends are performing a puppet show for their class. After doing research in the library to find out about puppets, each one had chosen a different style. They wrote a script and rehearsed for days. Now they are checking over their puppets a final time before their show.

1. Puppets have been in existence for hundreds of years. Marionettes have even been found in tombs in Egypt. Italian puppeteers traveled with their puppet theaters and puppets to other countries to perform. Write **Puppet Show Today** on the sign at the bottom of the puppet theater.

2. Tyrone chose to make a hand puppet of a frog. The hand puppet can also be called a glove puppet because it is placed over the hand. Write **hand puppet** on the frog. Then, color the frog green.

3. Max decided to make a shadow puppet of a bat. Rather than the audience seeing the actual puppet, they see the shadow of the puppet. In the box with the bat, write three words that rhyme with bat.

4. There is a bright light behind the screen to make the shadow. At the top left of the page, write a word that has the same ending as light.

5. Samantha liked the finger puppets because she could use her own fingers as the legs for her owl puppet. Color the owl brown and the beak and vest yellow.

6. Manfred's butterfly is a rod, or stick, puppet. One hand holds the rod that supports the puppet. Write **rod puppet** below the butterfly.

7. The butterfly's wings can be made to flutter using the two thin rods that you can hold in your other hand. Color the butterfly's wings using two of your favorite colors.

8. Calie's cat is a marionette which is moved by the strings that are attached to two controls, one for each hand. Very intricate marionettes can have more than thirty strings attached to various parts of the puppet! Calie's cat puppet has six strings. Write the name of a part of the body that has a string attached to it under the cat.

9. The bear is also a string puppet. Color the bear puppet brown and the cat puppet orange.

10. The backdrop, or scenery, helps the audience better understand the puppet show. On the back of this paper, draw and color what you think would be an appropriate backdrop for this puppet show.

## Follow-Up Fun

On the chalkboard, draw a picture of a camel marionette like the one shown. Have the students copy the camel and the questions and answer them. To give students extra practice, have them answer in complete sentences.

1. Which strings move the head?
2. Which strings move the camel's hump?
3. Strings g and f move which parts of the camel's body?
4. Which strings move the camel's front legs?
5. Which string moves the camel's head to the right?

30

31

# Humming Honeycombs

Reginald pours honey on just about everything he eats - pancakes, waffles, hot oatmeal and even ice cream! He will eat anything made with honey! His parents decided that because he liked honey so much, he should learn how it is made. Today, they are going to visit an apiary which is a place where beekeepers tend to their beehives.

1. Mr. Rex is an apiarian, or beekeeper. Write **beekeeper** on Mr. Rex's hat.

2. Honeybee hives, whether out in the wild or in manmade boxes, are filled with honeycombs. Each cell of a honeycomb has six sides. Color each row of honeycomb cells a different color.

3. Bees protect their hives. When disturbed, they fly about and defend themselves with a stinger. Twenty-two muscles in the bee's body are used when it stings. The hooks, or barbs, on the end of the stinger hold the stinger into whatever or whoever the bee stings. Draw a hook on the stinger of the big bee in the box. Write the number twenty-two on the bee.

4. To avoid being stung while handling the hives, Mr. Rex wears clothing that completely covers his body, making sure that there is no way for a bee to get up his shirt or pants' leg. He wears a hat with a veil of cloth or wire screen to protect his face. Draw a hat and veil of cloth to cover Reginald's head.

5. Sometimes, Mr. Rex wears gloves and other times, he doesn't. If he spends a lot of time working with the hives, honey quickly covers the gloves and makes them sticky. Color Mr. Rex's gloves yellow and his clothes brown.

6. To make honey, the worker bee must first find a source of nectar, a flower. This can be close to or far from the hive. Bees may have to travel up to a total of 13,000 miles, back and forth from the nectar source to the hive, to collect enough nectar for one pound of honey. To the left of the flower with the bee on it, write how many ounces are in a pound.

7. When it finds the flower, the bee uses its long tongue to suck the nectar from the flower. Color the flower petals purple and the middle yellow.

8. Until it returns to the hive, the nectar is stored in the bee's stomach. Once it reaches the hive, the bee gives the nectar to another bee by bringing the nectar back up through its mouth. That bee then places the nectar into one of the cells. To the right of the bee on the flower, write three words that end in ll.

9. The bee then tells the others in the hive where to find the nectar source. It moves in the same direction the other bees will have to fly in once they are outside the hive. Find the beehive on the platform. In which direction will the bee have to fly to get to the flower? Write the answer on the beehive. Then, color the hive yellow.

10. Honey is actually produced by chemicals in the honeybee's stomach. Once the nectar is in the cell, the water evaporates and the chemicals work to change the nectar to honey. Color the rest of the picture.

**Follow-Up Fun**
Honeybee is a compound word. Have the students fold both sides of a piece of paper in to the center. On the outside, they write a compound word. On the inside, they make a humorous drawing of it.

33

# Read a Rhyme

Everyone in Calie's class will have the opportunity to be a helper in kindergarten. Today, it is Calie's turn. Ms. LeChat, the kindergarten teacher, has asked Calie to read some nursery rhymes to the children. All of the children listen and imagine as Calie reads.

1.  The first rhyme Calie reads is thought to have been written by a pilgrim. It tells how Indians made cradles from the bark of birch trees. They used ropes to hang the cradles from tree limbs. Their babies rocked back and forth in the cradles. This rhyme is perhaps the first one to have been written on American soil. The name of this rhyme is "Hush-a-Bye." Color three cats orange.

2.  In the 1600's, a poem was written about a lady who rode horses in marathons. At that time, it was fashionable to wear shoes with long pointed toes. Part of the rhyme mentions the lady having bells on her toes. Draw a bell on the toe of the shoe one of the cats is thinking about. Write two words that rhyme with bell above the shoe.

3.  One day, a little girl would not allow anyone to curl her hair. Her father wrote a poem about it that day. Draw a curl hanging in the middle of the girl's forehead next to the shoe. Forehead is a compound word. Above the girl, write two compound words using the word day.

4.  What's dancing without music and singing? A silly, nonsensical rhyme was written for people to sing while doing a dance that was very popular at the time. The name of this poem is "Hey Diddle Diddle." Above the fiddle, draw what the cow jumps over.

5.  Today, we have rhymes to say while jumping rope. In the 1600's, a poem was written about a popular game that required a person to jump over a lit candle without putting out the flame. It was said that, if successful, he or she would have good luck. "Jack Be Nimble" is what the poem is called. Under the cat thinking about the candle, write a word that rhymes with stick.

6.  The next poem that Calie reads was written about the time a child was followed to school by her pet lamb. Under the cat thinking of the lamb, write the name of this poem.

7.  Anyone can write a rhyme. An entomologist, a person who studies insects, wrote a poem about his daughter. Draw a spider on Little Miss Muffet's stool. Color two cats black.

8.  The last rhyme that Calie reads has been popular for hundreds of years. The English even used the name of the main character to describe a clumsy person. Above the egg, write what "Humpty Dumpty" sat on.

9.  Draw a star on the picture of the poem you thought was most interesting. Color the last three cats brown. Write the number word of how many cats you colored above Calie's head.

10. Calie closes the book. Both she and the children enjoyed the rhymes. On the back of your paper, write a four-line poem. Draw a picture to illustrate your poem.

**Follow-Up Fun**

Have the students spend some time reading poetry anthologies looking for their all-time favorite poems. Then, have each student copy and illustrate his/her favorite. Put them together in a class book. In addition, have students record their poems. These tapes would be great in a listening center or to send on loan to a sick student.

35

# An Exciting Exchange

Chisai Ling and Calie have been pen pals for over a year. They have shared and learned a lot about each other's countries. When Calie opened the package from China, she was thrilled with the many wonderful and different gifts. One gift in particular, a poster, showed pictures of many things Chisai had written about in her letter.

1. China is located on the continent of Asia. Within China is a huge wall, built by hand, of earth, stone, bricks and lime. It was built for protection from invading armies, and it also served as a road. Appropriately, it is called The Great Wall. Write **The Great Wall** on the map.

2. Rice, one of the main foods of China, is grown in fields covered with water called paddies. In the box, color the water blue and the rice plant green.

3. Cone-shaped straw hats are worn by those who work in the rice paddies to provide them with some protection from the hot sun. Above the straw hat, draw three different shapes. Then, color the hat brown.

4. The figurine in the bottom right corner is an example of the oldest form of Chinese art - sculpture. At one time, sculptures were made from bronze, but later, jade was carved to create bowls, jars, statues and many other items. Color the figurine green. On the back of your paper, write **sculptures**. Then, write four new words using the letters in that word.

5. Throughout China, there are beautiful towerlike memorial buildings called pagodas. They are works of art with each of the many eight-sided stories being decorated with stonework and ivory. Write the number **eight** to the right of the pagoda. Color the pagoda grey.

6. On the poster is a small boat called a sampan. It is not only used as a means of traveling along the many rivers in China, but in many cases, it is also a home. A long pole, or oar, is used to row the sampan. Write **home** on the sampan. Color it brown and the water blue.

7. In China, a giant panda is called a beishung. No one outside of China knew of its existence until 1869. Write the date **1869** to the right of the panda. Then, to the left of the panda, write the year you were born.

8. This five-foot, 300-pound panda is covered with thick white fur except for its legs, ears, shoulders and the circles around its eyes which are black. On the stomach of the panda, write how tall it is in inches.

9. The giant panda lives in bamboo forests which are ideal because the panda's favorite food is bamboo. It eats more than 10,000 pounds of bamboo in a year. Under the panda, write how many zero's there are in the number ten thousand.

10. Calie is going to write a letter to Chisai to thank her for the gifts she sent. Write **thank you** at the top of the poster.

## Follow-Up Fun

Have students write make-believe letters to Chisai pretending that they are Calie. Instruct them to describe what it is like where they live, what they do for fun, what their homes are like, etc. Have students draw a picture of their favorite place in America. Then, mount the letters and pictures on construction paper for display.

China

37

# Picnic Perfection

What a wonderful day for a picnic! Calie has found the perfect spot for her and her friends.

1. Everyone is thirsty after carrying everything to the picnic site. Calie looks for the thermos bottle so she can pour everyone a glass of cold lemonade. The very first thermos was made in 1892 and was used to hold serums and vaccines. Draw a thermos in Calie's hand. On Calie's shirt, write how old the thermos is.

2. The frankfurter, or hot dog, originated about 3,500 years ago in Babylonia. The name frankfurter was first used in 1852 when the butchers in Frankfurt, Germany, developed a spicy sausage that closely resembles today's hot dog. They named it after their town. Write the name of another country in Europe on the blanket.

3. In the 1890's, a baker named Charles Feltman began cooking and selling frankfurter sandwiches at Coney Island. They were served on a roll and topped with sauerkraut and mustard. Draw a frankfurter in a roll on the plate. Use a yellow crayon to draw a squiggly line of mustard on the frankfurter.

4. What's a picnic without potato chips! If a Native American cook named George Crum hadn't gotten so upset with a picky diner in 1853, we may not have had this favorite snack today. The diner kept refusing the thick chunks of fried potatoes, so George cut them extremely thin and fried them extra crispy. Soon, everyone began ordering them. Draw a bag of potato chips in the basket.

5. For dessert, Calie brought a treat created in the 3rd century B.C. by the Romans. Back then, it was baked twice, which made it very hard, cut in squares and not at all sweet. Today's version of this soft and chewy treat came from the Dutch's small wedding cake called "Kioekje." Of course, it's cookies. Write the name of your favorite kind of cookie on the box in the lower left corner.

6. Time to clean up the mess! With the flick of the wrist, a brown paper bag opens for trash. Until 1883, when Charles Stilwell invented a machine to paste the paper bags together, they were hard to open and couldn't stand up because the bottom was pointed. Draw a paper bag to the right of the tree and color it brown.

7. Now it's time to have fun with a toy that was designed by a man named Walter Morrison who was fascinated by UFO's. Draw a Frisbee™ flying between the two cats at the top of the paper. Color the cats orange and yellow.

8. Max can do many tricks with a yo-yo. Although his is made of plastic, the first yo-yos in China were made of ivory and had a silk cord instead of string. Color Max's shirt blue and his yo-yo bright yellow.

9. Tyrone and Abby are playing marbles just as children in Egypt did 5,000 years ago. The Egyptians' marbles were made from semiprecious stones. Today, marbles are made from glass or agates. Color the marbles your favorite colors.

10. The wind is perfect for flying a kite. Over 3,000 years ago, the Chinese used kites to send coded messages between military forces by using different colors and designs. On the back of your paper, draw a kite with a coded message. Below your kite, write your coded message.

## Follow-Up Fun

Have students plan a picnic. List the following headings on the board instructing them to write 4 things under each.

•Things to Eat     •Things to Drink     •Things to Play With     •Places to Go

39

# Properly Packed

During vacation, Calie will be visiting her grandparents. They live on a ranch with lots of animals - even horses. Filled with excitement, she's carefully choosing the clothes and things needed for her visit.

1. Calie's new shirt fits perfectly with the length being just right to tuck in. Until the 1500's, a shirt was worn very loose and was long enough to at least cover one's knees. Write **It fits.** below Calie.

2. Shirts weren't always fastened with buttons. The first buttons, dating from about 200 B.C. until the 1200's, were sewn on clothes as decorations and types of jewelry. Clothes were fastened together with pins. To the left of Calie, write **decorations.** Using the letters in that word, make four new words on the back of your paper.

3. Blue jeans were first made in the 1850's by a tailor named Levi Strauss. The miners working their claims during the California gold rush were constantly wearing out their pants. Levi designed and sold pants made from the same material that was used for the miner's tent. Write the name of two states on Calie's jeans.

4. The canvas material of the blue jeans was very stiff so Levi began using a softer denim which he dyed with indigo blue color to help hide any stains. Color Calie's blue jeans dark blue.

5. Calie's boots with the short heel will be perfect for helping keep her foot in the stirrup when she goes horseback riding. Boots first appeared in 1100 B.C. and were worn by soldiers going into battle. Color Calie's boots and her vest light brown.

6. Pajamas were not always a matched shirt and pants. Originally, the top was a long nightshirt for sleeping and the baggy pants were worn for relaxing at home. Color the pajama top and pants on Calie's bed your favorite color.

7. When not horseback riding, Calie plans to wear her white sneakers. The name sneaker was given to this shoe style because the rubber sole allowed a person to walk and not be heard, or sneak around. Write **sneaker** between the two shoes.

8. Now that the clothes have been decided upon, Calie thinks about the other items she will pack in the smaller bag, like her brush and comb. Her comb is made of a nylon material. But, from artifacts found dating around the year 4000 B.C., it is known that combs were made back then by drying the backbone or spine of a large fish. Draw a fish around the comb.

9. Don't forget your toothbrush, Calie! It's not an electric one, but it is certainly a lot softer than the first toothbrushes. Around 1498, toothbrushes were made from the stiff bristles of hogs. Calie's is also a lot quicker to use than the silver or brass toothpicks that were popular at one time. How old would a toothbrush be today that was made in 1498? Write the answer above Calie's bed.

10. Oops! Almost forgot! No one goes to a ranch without a cowboy hat. Actually, it's called a Stetson for the man who designed it in the 1860's. Even though it was originally designed for the very rich cattle barons or kings, the Stetson became, and still is, very popular with many people. The Stetson is a very large hat and has thus been labeled the ten-gallon hat. Write **10 gallons** on Calie's hat.

40

41

# Off to the Aquarium!

Calie's class has just finished studying a science unit about water habitats. So, today they went on a field trip to an aquarium. Manfred Manx is more excited than the others because his father works at the aquarium. Manfred has learned a lot of interesting facts about the different animals from his father. Even though everyone is busy looking at the animals in the tanks, they are also listening carefully to the information their classmate is sharing with them.

1. A crab is a decapod which means it has ten limbs. It has eight legs for walking and two pincers, or claws, for capturing food. Its back is reddish-brown, its legs are a dark red, and its claws are black. Color the crab.

2. Crabs live in shallow water off rocky coastlines. They spend much of their time buried in the sand or lying on small rocks. Coastline is a compound word. Below Calie, write two compound words.

3. The most common species of starfish have five arms, but others can have only four or as many as fifty. Draw a starfish with five arms below the crab.

4. Starfish can be many different colors. Most often, they are yellow, orange, pink or red. But, there are a few that are grey, blue, green or purple. In the water, write two colors that the starfish can be. Color the starfish purple.

5. One kind of creature that lives in the ocean and looks more like a tree than an animal is coral. It has a hard skeleton that is covered by flesh on which the polyps grow. This is another brightly colored sea animal. Color the coral bright orange.

6. One animal that looks like a snake is called an electric eel because it gives off electric shocks. It can give a shock of up to 550 volts of electricity. In the cave, draw an eel and color it greenish brown. Draw four zigzag shock lines coming from its body.

7. Electric eels have three electricity-producing organs, two small and one large. Even when resting, the smallest organ near the tip of the tail gives off electricity. Just like a battery, an eel is negatively and positively charged. A negative charge is given off near the tail, and a positive charge is given off near the head. Draw a minus sign near the tail and a plus sign near the head of the eel.

8. The sea turtle ranks among the largest of the turtle species. A leatherback turtle may measure up to eight feet and weigh as much as 1,500 pounds. On the turtle's shell, write how many inches are in eight feet.

9. A sea turtle cannot hide in its shell like other turtles. It depends on its size and its swimming speed for defense. Color the turtle brown and yellow.

10. Jellyfish is the perfect name for this animal. It's shaped like an umbrella and is practically all water or jelly. Most have either four or eight tentacles hanging from their bodies, but some have many more. Draw eight tentacles hanging from the jellyfish. Color the jellyfish white with a dark purple rim along the bottom of the body.

## Follow-Up Fun

Write the following on the chalkboard for an Activity of the Day. To make it easier for visitors to find certain animals, there is often a directory that lists the animals and tells where they can be found in the aquarium. Make a sign that lists the following animal names in ABC order: electric eel, crab, octopus, starfish, jellyfish, coral, sea horse, whale, sea turtle, dolphin, anemone, squid.

43

# Catch Sight of a Kite

All the kids have been waiting to try out their new kites. It has seemed like there would never be a day with a good kite-flying breeze. But . . . today is perfect!

1.  Kites have been flying in the sky since 1200 B.C. Write the date **1200 B.C.** at the top of the page.

2.  One member of the hawk family is called a kite. Perhaps today's word kite originated from the graceful way this hawk soars through the sky. Write three words that rhyme with kite in the sky.

3.  Shapes, sizes and designs of kites and even materials used for making kites are constantly changing as more and more people are enjoying the activity. The simplest design is two crossed sticks forming a diamondlike shape. On the back of your paper, design a diamond-shaped kite and color it using bright colors.

4.  The Chinese dragon kite is made of several sections. The first section is the dragon's head. Color the dragon's head yellow and color a red flame coming from its mouth.

5.  The other section of the dragon kite represents its body. Because it is such a large kite, several people are needed to fly it. Color the dragon's body green. Color the spikes, or wings, orange.

6.  Have you ever heard a kite whistle? That sound is made by several small holes in the kite's surface. On the kite that is shaped like a bat, draw a hole in each triangle.

7.  Isn't it fun to watch all the bright, beautiful colors swaying and soaring in the sky? Color the box-shaped kite using two of your favorite bright colors.

8.  Kites were not always just toys. They have been used in experiments to learn about weather, as targets for gunnery practice and even to carry the first line across the Niagara Falls to start the construction of a suspension bridge across it. Write **not just a kite** below the box-shaped kite.

9.  In China, there is a special day called Kite Day on which everyone flies kites. This celebration began from the legend about a man who had a dream that on a specific day, his house would be destroyed. When that day came, he and his family went out to the countryside and had fun flying kites. When they arrived back home, they found their house totally destroyed. But, most importantly, he and his family were alive and safe. Kite Day is always the ninth day of the ninth month. Write that month's name in the upper right corner of the paper. Color the last kite purple with red streamers.

10. No matter what you do to have fun, you need to remember safety - even when flying kites. Being safe keeps a fun time filled with fun. Among the basic kite flying rules are: never use any metal in your kite, never fly a kite near wires or electrical towers, and never fly a kite during a thunderstorm. Write **Always Be Safe** on the bat-shaped kite. Color Calie orange and her friend brown.

## Follow-Up Fun
Have students design a very special kite for Chinese Kite Day. Provide all different colors of construction paper, tissue paper and scraps of cloth. Hang the finished kites from the ceiling to make a colorful display. You could also take the kites outside and fly them to see if they work.

44

45

# Ixi's Outing

Some people are frightened by a reptile's prehistoric appearance. Calie isn't! As a matter of fact, she even has a reptile as a pet. Calie has brought her pet iguana, named Ixi, to school with her. Maybe her classmates will learn that some reptiles are not as scary as they look.

1. Iguanas, such as Ixi, can be found in Central Amercia and in the northern part of South America. Color North Amercia green and South America yellow on the globe. Don't forget to color the oceans blue.

2. Ixi is a green iguana and blends in well with the tropical forest of his homeland. The tropical forest provides an iguana with lots of trees to climb. Although he may not look like it, Ixi is an excellent climber. Color Ixi and his small tropical tree green.

3. When Ixi isn't walking around the house, he stays in a large plastic box called a terrarium. Draw a box on the bottom shelf of the bookcase.

4. Since Calie's house isn't as warm as Ixi's natural tropical climate, she bought a special rock. When plugged in, the rock heats up and provides a very warm spot for Ixi. Color the rock red and the electrical cord black.

5. Ixi's appearance is part of his defense. If threatened or frightened, he will inflate his throat sac and make his crest, the fringe along his back, stand up. Draw an arrow pointing upward on Ixi's crest. To the right of the tree, write three words using the letters in appearance.

6. Once an iguana has made itself look as big and ferocious as it can, it runs! Write **come back** in the terrarium.

7. Ixi is an herbivore, which is a plant eater. He likes to eat leaves, plant shoots, fruit and flowers. Draw a flower near Ixi's mouth.

8. Because he is still a young iguana, Ixi will sometimes eat insects. Write **bugs** on the jar.

9. Young iguanas grow very slowly and may even take two years to mature. But some iguanas live for 30 years or more. On top of the bug jar, write how many months are in two years.

10. When Ixi was born, he was only ten inches long. By the time he is full grown, he may be as long as six feet! Write **six feet** beside the tip of Ixi's tail. Under Ixi's tail, write how many inches are in six feet.

## Follow-Up Fun

Write the following on the chalkboard for the students to copy, or cut the directions out and copy them.

### Comparable Comparisons

Read each phrase. Think about how it can be described. Finish each sentence by comparing its subject to something else.
1. Ixi the Iguana is as green as . . .
2. Gusts of wind whirled through the trees like . . .
3. His aching tooth felt like . . .
4. The puppet strings were as tangled as . . .
5. Gold nuggets are as shiny as . . .
6. Everyone jumped into the cool water like . . .
7. Trying to remember the correct answer is as hard as . . .
8. Peanut butter sticks to your mouth like . . .

47

_____
name

# is "cat"apulting to good listening skills!

_____
teacher

_____
date

_____
name

# "Cat"ches this award for good listening!

_____
teacher

_____
date